Hello,
My Name Is ...

Barkley

By Wally Elliott

Courier Publishing
100 Manly Street
Greenville, South Carolina 29601
CourierPublishing.com

PUBLISHED IN THE UNITED STATES OF AMERICA

Dedicated to all of our dog and horse friends that our animals have brought into our lives. We thank the Good Lord for all of you regularly.

Oil and incense bring joy to the heart, and the sweetness of a friend is better than self-counsel. (Proverbs 27:9)

Acknowledgments

To my wife, Angie, who has always stood
behind me and always supported my
crazy ideas of living out dreams.

A wife of noble character is her husband's crown.
(Proverbs 12:4)

To my grandsons, Kam, Rome and Hunter,
and the one on the way: I pray you will
always look to the Lord for guidance.

Start a youth out on his way; even when he grows
old he will not depart from it. (Proverbs 22:6)

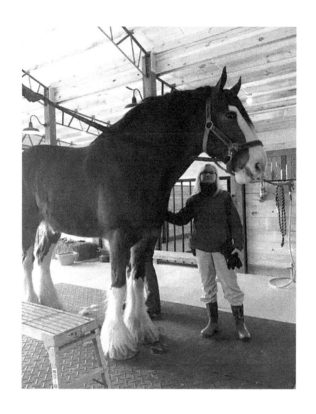

Chapter 1

Hello, my name is Barkley. I'm a Clydesdale horse. I'd like to tell you a little bit about me, but first I'd like to tell you about my horse family that goes back a long, long time ago. My great-great-great grandparents came from a country far away named Scotland. There is a river that runs through Scotland where my ancestors came from, and its name is the Clyde River; that's how we got our name "Clydesdale." We get to be really big, over six feet at our withers — which is our back area at the base of our neck — and we weigh 2,000 pounds or more. Another thing that we are really famous for is the beautiful, feathery hair around our feet.

Way back then, before there were trucks and tractors, the farmers used the very strong Clydesdales for helping them work, such as pulling plows in the field and pulling heavy loads, like logs and loaded wagons.

In today's times, many people use us for showing at Draft Horse Shows, pulling carriages or just having us as a part of a farm family. We are sometimes called "gentle giants" because we are really big, and we are very gentle and sweet.

Barkley's Bible School Notes

God made all animals, including horses like Barkley, for people to enjoy and to use to bring glory to His name.

Bible Verse: Genesis 1:24-25

[24] Then God said, "Let the earth produce living creatures according to their kinds: livestock, creatures that crawl, and the wildlife of the earth according to their kinds." And it was so. [25] So God made the wildlife of the

earth according to their kinds, the livestock according to their kinds, and all the creatures that crawl on the ground according to their kinds. And God saw that it was good.

2017 Royal Winter Fair
Reserve Grand Champion Gelding

Chapter 2

Now, let me tell you a little about me. I was once part of a "team" of horses that traveled all over the United States and Canada competing in halter events and hitch events.

At halter events, all I had to do was go out into a big show arena and walk alongside and run alongside my handler. A judge would look at me and all of the other Clydesdales and give ribbons to the winners. One year, at the Royal Fair in Canada, I was chosen as the runner-up to the Champion Clydesdale in my class. Then, later on, at the Ohio State Fair, I was chosen as the Champion Clydesdale in my class. I was really proud and held my head up high and pranced very gracefully when the crowd stood up and clapped as I was paraded around the arena.

When I was part of the "Hitch Team," I traveled all over the country, along with five other of my stable mates. We would be hitched to a beautiful Hitch Wagon, lined up two abreast. I was the lead horse for our team. It was my job to set a good example for the other horses to follow.

As I became older, around ten years old, my owner decided to let me take it easy from all the traveling and the hard work it took to be a competition horse, and he let me retire. My owner loved me very much, so instead of me just going out into the pasture every day and being bored, he decided he would search for a home for me that I could be part of as a new family member.

This is where the story gets really cool … some amazing things began to take place. At first the story is a little sad, but it all works out with happy times.

In South Carolina, there was a horse named Cinnamon. Cinnamon was a very special horse that was loved dearly by her owner. People would often stop by the barn where Cinnamon lived and offer to buy her from her owner. You see, Cinnamon is a very beautiful Buckskin Quarter Horse. Cinnamon's owner would always smile real big and tell them, "Nope, no amount of money can buy Cinnamon. She's gonna stay right here." One day her owner became very sick and could no longer give Cinnamon all the love and attention that she needed. During this time, the lady at the neighboring farm would check on Cinnamon to make sure she had fresh water and hay. Her name was Mrs. Angie Elliott, and she enjoyed making sure Cinnamon was okay. One sad day, Cinnamon's owner passed away. Before he passed away, he told his son to ask Mrs. Angie if Cinnamon could go live with her on her farm, which was called the "Diamond E Farm." Mrs. Angie and her husband, Mr. Wally Elliott, told the son they would need to pray about the decision they would need to make. They prayed that night, and the next morning they called the son and told him they would be honored to let Cinnamon come live with them on their farm.

There was one problem. Mrs. Angie and Mr. Wally did not have a horse barn at their farm. So they asked their friend, Miss Pat, to keep Cinnamon until they could get a barn built. She lived not too far away on a farm that had lots of stalls and was really good at taking care of horses. This is where the story starts getting me involved, and no one even knew about me yet.

Barkley's Bible School Notes

Any time we have tough decisions to make, we need to make sure to talk to God about them by praying and asking Him to help us make those decisions.

Bible Verse: Philippians 4:6

[6] Don't worry about anything, but in everything, through prayer and petition with thanksgiving, present your requests to God.

Chapter 3

The Elliott family started building their horse barn. The size of the barn had to be decided. One very important consideration would be how many horses would live at their new barn. The Elliotts knew that horses were much happier when they had a friend and didn't live alone. So now, they were thinking of building the barn large enough to have a friend or maybe a couple of friends for Cinnamon. As they thought about this, they agreed they had always loved all the wonderful stories they had heard about the Clydesdale horses. Listen carefully, because now the story is getting even closer to when I get involved. The Elliotts decided that Cinnamon's new friend would be a Clydesdale horse.

With that, the Elliotts talked to many Clydesdale owners about the barn they were about to build. They were told that a Clydesdale requires a special barn. Everything has to be bigger and more heavy duty. The stalls had to be larger and taller. The stall gates had to be wider, and the poles needed to be bigger. The food containers needed to be larger, and there had to be a special storage area called the "tack room" to keep all the harness equipment that you would use to put on a Clydesdale horse if you had a cart or a carriage.

With all this information, the horse barn construction started and eventually was finished and ready for a horse or horses to move in.

Barkley's Bible School Notes

Mr. Wally and Mrs. Angie had lots of instructions on building the horse barn. It was important that they followed those instructions. God gave Noah instructions on how to build the ark, and he listened very carefully. God still gives us instructions in how He wants us to live. These instructions are in your Bible.

Bible Verse: Genesis 6:14-16

[14] "Make yourself an ark of gopher wood. Make rooms in the ark, and cover it with pitch inside and outside. [15] This is how you are to make it: The ark will be 450 feet long, 75 feet wide, and 45 feet high. [16] You are to make a roof, finishing the sides of the ark to within eighteen inches of the roof. You are to put a door in the side of the ark. Make it with lower, middle, and upper decks.

Chapter 4

While the barn was being built, Mrs. Angie and Mr. Wally were all excited about looking for a Clydesdale horse that could be a new family member to them, their nine Labrador Retrievers, their Coon Dog, and Cinnamon. Meanwhile, Miss Pat brought Cinnamon from her temporary home, and Cinnamon was shown her new forever home. The search for the Clydesdale horse continued every day with no luck. Mrs. Angie and Mr. Wally were beginning to get discouraged until one day Miss Shelby, another of Mrs. Angie's friends, talked to Mrs.

Angie and told her she would help her find a Clydesdale. This was very exciting news because Miss Shelby owned Clydesdales, and she had lots of friends who owned Clydesdales too. Miss Shelby was even a hitch driver for one of the most famous Clydesdale teams ever.

Only a day later, Mr. Wally got a call from Mrs. Angie. She said, "Come up to the barn right away. Miss Shelby just sent me a picture, and I want you to see it." When Mr. Wally got to the barn, he looked at the picture and his jaw dropped. He said, "That's the most amazing horse I have ever seen." They frantically got back in touch with Miss Shelby and asked her a whole lot of questions about the horse in the picture. They wanted to know everything there was to know about this amazing horse.

Miss Shelby put Mrs. Angie and Mr. Wally in touch with Mr. Eric; he was a manager of a farm in Ohio, and he was in charge of this special horse.

The owner of the farm had farms in Ohio and Canada. On their farm they had Clydesdales — and they took their Clydesdales all over Canada and the United States, competing in Clydesdale halter and hitch team events. They had a special horse that they were considering letting him retire if they could find just the right place for him to live.

Are things starting to sound familiar? That's right … the special horse that Miss Shelby found … was me! Yep, that amazing horse in the picture that made Mr. Wally's jaw drop … was me — Barkley!

Mr. Eric decided that Mrs. Angie and Mr. Wally would be the perfect forever home for me. Miss Shelby was so excited about this wonderful news that she offered to take her giant horse trailer rig from where she lived in Indiana and pick me up in Ohio. Then we would begin the journey down to South Carolina to the Diamond E Farm.

Barkley's Bible School Notes

God is always at work planning wonderful things for our lives.

Bible Verse: Jeremiah 29:11

[11] "For I know the plans I have for you" — this is the LORD'S declaration — "plans for your well-being, not for disaster, to give you a future and a hope."

Chapter 5

We traveled for a couple of days, and this trip was a little different for me. Normally, I would be traveling with our whole team, but this time I was all alone. Finally, Miss Shelby turned her big rig off the main highway onto the long driveway of the Diamond E Farm. I could see green barns, lots of ponds, and some plush green pastures. We pulled around to one of the barns and I could hear people talking. They sounded very excited, and when Miss Shelby opened the rear trailer gate to let me out, I could hear even more excitement. I backed out of the trailer and put my feet on the ground that would become my new home. There was a group of people there to welcome me, but the first two people I saw were Mrs. Angie and Mr. Wally. They were my new owners, and I could tell they loved me at first sight. It was really cool for me too. I had no idea what wonderful things were in store for me at the Diamond E Farm. Everyone gathered around and rubbed me and loved on me. Mrs. Angie is a little, teeny lady, and I had to lean my head way down so she could give me a "welcome to the Diamond E Farm" kiss right on my nose. I had been standing in the trailer for a long time, so we went for a walk so I could stretch my legs.

When we got back to the barn, Mr. Wally brought out a brand-new, shiny harness. He had ordered it from his friend named Mr. Bob. It was made just for me, and Mr. Wally and Miss Shelby put it on me and adjusted it so it felt very comfortable. Then I got hitched up to a cart and went for my first drive at my new home. Afterwards, we went back to the barn, and Mr. Wally took my harness off and led me inside. It was then that I saw another horse about half my size.

Barkley's Bible School Notes

There are times that we are a little afraid when we have to experience new things, but God tells us not to be afraid. He tells us He is right there with us, and He will never leave us.

Bible Verse: Deuteronomy 31:6

⁶ Be strong and courageous; don't be terrified or afraid of them. For the LORD your God is the one who will go with you; he will not leave you or abandon you."

Chapter 6

She was a buckskin brown color, and when she saw me she let out a big whinny. At first, I didn't know if she was going to like me, but she came up to me, whinnied again and moved her head up and down. It was as if she was saying, "I'm so glad to have a friend join me at the farm." I learned her name was Cinnamon, and we would have the barn and the paddock all to ourselves. We would become great friends, and everywhere I went she would be close by. We very seldom get a long way apart, unless it starts raining. I love to stand out in the rain and feel the cool water on my back. But Cinnamon can feel one little drop on her back and she heads for the barn. Then she just stands inside and looks at me out of her window, wondering why I'm not inside too.

As the day went on, I was later introduced to some more Diamond E Farm animals. Mrs. Angie came over to my barn later with her nine Labrador Retrievers and a Coon Dog. I got a little nervous again, just like when I met Cinnamon for the first time. They all seemed very eager to get over near me, and I was relieved to see how nice they were. Not a single one nipped at me. Instead, they all seemed so happy to see me, and they all wanted to touch noses with me. I could already tell they were going to be some awesome friends. Later that day, just before the sun set, Mr. Wally came over and put my halter on me, and Mrs. Angie put Cinnamon's halter on her.

They took us out of our paddock, and all of us, including my dog friends, went for a long walk around the Diamond E Farm. We walked around the ponds, across some more pastures and through some woods. They let me stop every now and then and just look around at all the beautiful surroundings. I was liking the farm and all my new friends more and more. As we walked, Mrs. Angie kept calling the dogs and told them not to get near my huge feet, but I was being very careful and made sure I didn't accidentally step on one of them. She kept calling them by name, and I was trying to remember them, but there were so many. There was Grace, the grandma. Blaze and Reverend were her sons, and Faith and Lilly were her daughters. Then, as if I wasn't confused enough, there were Lilly's sons, Soldier and Rock — and Lilly's daughters, Olive and Promise. Oh, and don't forget the Coon Dog. Her name is Walker.

That evening as the sun went down, a big full moon came up over the Diamond E Farm. It was quiet and so peaceful. The moonlight made everything so pretty. I stood just outside my stable door and was thankful for my new home and my new family.

Barkley's Bible School Notes

Barkley met a lot of new friends. He learned they were all very nice. He couldn't help but love them. That's what the Bible says we are supposed to do.

Bible Verse: Mark 12:30-31

[30] Love the Lord your God with all your heart, with all your soul, with all your mind, and with all your strength. [31] The second is, Love your neighbor as yourself. There is no other command greater than these."

Chapter 7

The next few weeks had some really awesome things happening at the Diamond E Farm. One day Mr. Wally and Mrs. Angie had a really big, church-wide picnic at the farm. People of all ages were all over the farm, eating, playing games and singing. I'll have to say, I was a pretty big hit too. Mr. Wally put my halter on and let me out in front of my barn. Everyone was wanting to give me treats and have their picture made with me. It was a lot of fun, and I liked hearing the little ones chuckle when I nibbled the treat out of their hand. Cinnamon was a little shy around the people at first, but after she saw how nice they were to me and how I was getting bunches of treats, she quickly became very social and learned how to nudge folks and let them know that she liked treats too.

Another time that made me feel really good was when a family came out to visit and just say hello to me. One little boy in the family didn't have any hair, and he seemed sad. I couldn't help but keep walking over to him and nudging him with my nose. He liked for me to do that, and he told his mom that he thought I must like him. His mom agreed and said she thought I wanted to be his special friend. It made the little boy smile really big. His mom got some tears in her eyes and said, "My goodness, I haven't seen that beautiful smile in a long time." Later, I heard the mom tell Mrs. Angie and Mr. Wally that her son had been very sick, and the medicine he had to take made him feel really bad too. I was glad to help the little fella be happy. It made me feel all warm and happy inside too!

Barkley's Bible School Notes

Barkley made the little boy smile by just being nice and friendly to him. We can do the same for others around us.

Bible Verse: Hebrews 13:16

[16] Don't neglect to do what is good and to share, for God is pleased with such sacrifices.

Chapter 8

One of the things I like to do is stand at my fence and watch Mrs. Angie and all the dogs train for what Labrador Retrievers do. Mrs. Angie will throw an object that she calls a training bumper. After she throws it, the dogs will have to wait until she calls their name, and then that dog will get to run out and bring back the training bumper. They come right back, sit by her side, and hold their heads up to let her take the training bumper. Then she will throw it again and call a different name. She will do this until all the dogs have a turn at retrieving the training bumper. I was amazed at how well they listen to Mrs. Angie and how much they want to obey her and please her. Then one day I overheard Pastor Robbie ask Mr. Wally and Mrs. Angie if they could have the Community Thanksgiving Program at the Diamond E Farm. He also asked Mrs. Angie if she could let all the folks in the community see how well her dogs retrieved, how obedient they were, and how they liked to please her. They said yes, and I was looking forward to seeing that myself.

Barkley's Bible School Notes

Barkley was amazed at how well-behaved Mrs. Angie's dogs were. They were very obedient, and you could tell they love her very much. God wants us to be like Mrs. Angie's dogs. He wants us to love Him and be obedient to Him.

Bible Verse: John 14:21

[21] "The one who has my commands and keeps them is the one who loves me. And the one who loves me will be loved by my Father. I also will love him and will reveal myself to him."

Chapter 9

In a few days, Mr. Wally walked into the barn with a friend. His name was Mr. Rexx. Mr. Wally came into my stall, and rubbed my ears, which I really like. He said, "Barkley, Mr. Rexx is here to help me make sure I'm a good driver. We are going to use you, along with the dogs, in the Thanksgiving Program." I couldn't imagine how I could do anything as wonderful as the dogs did, but Mr. Wally whispered in my ear, "Barkley, you are a very special boy, and you have your own talents. They're not the same as the dogs, but they are still very special. Here's what we're gonna do. I have taken the duck boat that Mrs. Angie uses for training with the dogs, and I'm going to put wheels on the bottom of it. Then I'm going to hitch the duck boat to the back of your cart. Mrs. Angie and the dogs are going to sit in the duck boat, and I'm going to drive you over to where the crowd will be gathered in the pasture. There will be a lot of people there, and that's why Mr. Rexx is here — to make sure I'm a good driver and can drive you through all those folks safely."

After Mr. Wally whispered that in my ear, he looked at me in the eyes, and he looked a little nervous. He said, "Do you think you can do that, Barkley?" I thought to myself, "Wow, this will be a piece of cake." Where I came from, I have been in parades, pulled my cart through all sorts of people in cart events, and helped my other horse buddies pull a big wagon in a huge show arena full of people. I wasn't nearly as nervous as Mr. Wally. When the big day came, cars and trucks started lining up and driving into the main gate at the farm.

They parked and gathered over at the part of the pasture where Mrs. Angie would make her dog presentation. Once everybody was in place, Mr. Wally put my fancy harness on me and hitched me to my cart. Then Mrs. Angie told all the dogs to get in the duck boat and sit in their places. Then Mrs. Angie got in the duck boat, too, and they hitched it to my cart. When everyone was in place, Mr. Wally firmly said, "AWRIGHT." That was my command to start walking and pulling. As we were getting closer to the crowd, I could see everyone smiling. They thought it was really cool to see a Clydesdale pull a duck boat with five Labradors and a little lady in it.

Mr. Wally guided me with the lines connected to my bridle through the crowd toward our spot in the pasture. Just before we got to the spot where we were supposed to stop, a little, tiny boy ran out in front of me. He stopped and looked up at me. I'm sure he had never seen an animal as big as me. There was a lot of chatter going on with the folks who had gathered, but suddenly you could hear a pin drop! Mr. Wally let out a shaky, "Whoa, Barkley." Before he ever got that out of his mouth, I realized that this little fellow had slipped away from his mom. I stopped in my tracks and leaned my head way down. The little boy's mom was standing to the side with her hands across her eyes. The little fellow walked up to me and patted me on my nose. Then his mom scooped him up and looked back at me as if to say, "Thank you for being such a gentle giant and watching out for my little boy."

Once we got into place, we began the program. I was so proud to be involved in the message that was delivered. Mr. Wally and Mrs. Angie used their dogs and me as an example of how important it is for me and the Labs to be obedient to them. They explained that Jesus wanted us to love Him and be obedient to Him too. It was really cool to use my special talent to help others learn about Jesus.

Barkley's Bible School Notes

Barkley knew that Mrs. Angie's dogs had a special talent. He soon realized he had a special talent too. His talent was different from the dogs, but God helped Barkley use his talents in a very special way.

Bible Verse: 1 Peter 4:10-11

[10] Just as each one has received a gift, use it to serve others, as good stewards of the varied grace of God. [11] If anyone speaks, let it be as one who speaks God's words; if anyone serves, let it be from the strength God provides, so that God may be glorified through Jesus Christ in everything. To him be the glory and the power forever and ever. Amen.

Chapter 10

Once the program was over, everyone was invited over to my barn to take pictures with me. What a great day this was. When the sun went down, I got ready for sleep time. I paused and thanked Jesus for being able to be a part of the program today, and I hoped in some little way I made someone happy — as happy as me! What a wonderful blessing it was going to be to get to spend some amazing days like this on the Diamond E Farm.

Barkley's Bible School Notes

Barkley felt really blessed after the program was over. He realized that he was going to have a wonderful life at the Diamond E Farm.

Mrs. Angie and I hope you realize the Lord has blessings for you as well. We pray that you have learned a little something by reading this book … something very powerful!

Bible Verse: Numbers 6:24-26

[24] "May the LORD bless you and protect you;
[25] may the LORD make his face shine on you
and be gracious to you;
[26] may the LORD look with favor on you
and give you peace."'

The End … for now.